# Ultimate FACTIVITY Collection
# DINOSAURS

## Create your own book about the prehistoric world

**DK**

LONDON, NEW YORK, MUNICH,
MELBOURNE, AND DELHI

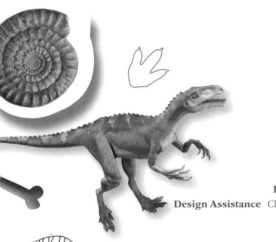

**Editor** James Mitchem
**Senior Designer** Clare Shedden
**Designers** Ria Holland, Yumiko Tahata
**Design Assistance** Charlotte Bull, Glenda Fisher, Elaine Hewson, Charlotte Johnson
**Editorial Assistance** Ellie de Rose
**Consultant** Darren Naish
**Jacket Designers** Ria Holland, Rosie Levine, Natasha Rees
**Illustrators** Helen Dodsworth, Chris Howker, Barney Ibbotson, Jake McDonald

**Pre-Production Producer** Sarah Isle
**Senior Producer** Alex Bell
**Creative Technical Support** Sonia Charbonnier
**Managing Editor** Penny Smith
**Senior Managing Art Editor** Marianne Markham
**Publisher** Mary Ling
**Creative Director** Jane Bull

First published in Great Britain in 2014 by
Dorling Kindersley Limited
80 Strand, London WC2R 0RL
1 2 3 4 5 6 7 8 9 10
001–196311–Apr14

A CIP catalogue record for this book is available from the British Library.

ISBN: 978-1-4093-4836-8
Printed and bound in China by L. Rex Printing Co., Ltd.
Discover more at **www.dk.com**

# The prehistoric world

Long ago, before humans ever existed, amazing creatures called dinosaurs roamed the Earth. These incredible reptiles are one of history's greatest treasures.

Page _____

Page _____

Page _____

Page _____

Page _____

Page _____

**FIND** these pictures on pages 4–17 and write the page numbers in the boxes.

## MATCH

the name of each dinosaur with its meaning by studying the clues.

### What do these names mean?

- Tyrannosaurus rex
- Stegosaurus
- Gallimimus
- Oviraptor
- Velociraptor
- Triceratops

**1** Roof lizard

"Saurus" means lizard.

**2** Egg thief

"Ovi" means egg in Latin.

**3** Chicken mimic

I wonder what raptor means...

**4** Speedy thief

**5** Three-horned face

Psst. "Tri" means three.

**6** Tyrant lizard king

# What did they look like?

Big, small, and everything in between, dinosaurs came in all shapes and sizes. Do you think you can draw them accurately?

## STEGOSAURUS

- Walked on all fours, low to the ground.
- Had short front legs and longer back legs with hoof-like toes.
- A double row of diamond-shaped plates ran down its neck, back, and long tail.
- Its head was narrow with a beak-like mouth.

**SIZE GUIDE**

## TRICERATOPS

- Walked on all fours with short, thick legs.
- Had a large, bony crest that looked like a collar covering its skull.
- Had two large horns above its eyes and a smaller one by its nose.
- It had a rhino-like body.

**SIZE GUIDE**

## DRAW

each dinosaur in the frames by using the clues as a guide, but be creative!

### EORAPTOR

- Walked and ran on its strong back legs.
- It wasn't much bigger than a chicken, but had a large head.
- Had sharp claws.

**SIZE GUIDE**

### BRACHIOSAURUS

- Its gigantic body was supported by thick, strong legs.
- A very long neck helped it reach treetops for food.
- It had a very long and thick tail.
- Its head was small for its size, with a bump on top.

**SIZE GUIDE**

Leg bone

Can you find all these dinosaurs in this book?

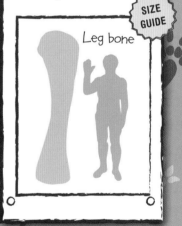

5

# The Mesozoic Era

COLOUR the dinosaurs and pterosaurs for all three periods of the Mesozoic Era.

Dinosaurs are one of the most successful creatures to ever exist. They ruled the Earth for about 186 million years during a time called the Mesozoic Era.

The Mesozoic Era was split up into three periods.

Herrerasaurus

Coelophysis

Lesothosaurus

Mussaurus

## Pangaea

At the start of the Mesozoic Era, Earth's continents were all joined together into one big land mass called **Pangaea** (All Earth). Over millions of years they broke up to form the continents we know today.

**TRUE OR FALSE?**
T. REX LIVED CLOSER IN TIME TO HUMANS THAN IT DID TO EARLY DINOSAURS.

## The Triassic
251–200 million years ago

Oviraptor

Archaeopteryx

Pterodactylus

Brachiosaurus

Tyrannosaurus rex

Pachycephalosaurus

Stegosaurus

Triceratops

Iguanodon

Spinosaurus

Velociraptor

**The Cretaceous**
145–65 million years ago

**The Jurassic**
200–145 million years ago

Humans don't arrive
for millions of years!

## The first dinosaurs

### Plateosaurus
**PLATE-ee-oh-SORE-us**
At 8m (25ft) long,
Plateosaurus was one
of the biggest dinosaurs
from the Triassic.

### Herrerasaurus
**Her-RARE-uh-SORE-us**
This early meat-eater
lived 228 million
years ago, but was only
discovered in 1961CE.

### Thecodontosaurus
**THEE-co-DON-toe-SORE-us**
One of the first
dinosaurs to be
discovered, its name
means "socket-tooth lizard".

### Pisanosaurus
**PIE-san-uh-SORE-us**
At only 1m (3ft)
long, Pisanosaurus
was the first known
"bird-hipped" dinosaur.

### Eoraptor
**EE-oh-rap-tor**
About the size of a
fox, Eoraptor used its
sharp claws and teeth
to help catch its prey.

# Triassic
## period

Find the stickers
by colour and shape

**STICK**
the stickers next to
the descriptions and fill
the rest of the scene
with dinosaurs.

The first period in the Mesozoic Era was called the Triassic. It spanned from 251–200 million years ago, and was the time when the first dinosaurs emerged.

Dinosaurs weren't very big during the Triassic period.

**TRUE OR FALSE?**
THE DINOSAUR STEGOSAURUS LIVED DURING THE TRIASSIC PERIOD.

Facts about...

## Earth

The planet looked very different during the Triassic. Because it was so much **hotter and drier**, there weren't many plants, and most of the land was covered in desert.

9

# Jurassic period

During the Jurassic period the planet grew a lot cooler. This allowed more trees and plants to grow, and was one of the reasons so many new species of dinosaur emerged.

**SPOT** the five differences between the two pictures of the sauropods.

Sauropods like me are the biggest creatures to ever walk on land!

Brachiosaurus, one of the largest sauropods, grew to up to 23m (75ft) long!

# Sauropods

These dinosaurs emerged during the Jurassic period. They were giants with **long tails and necks**, which helped them reach leaves to eat from the tops of tall trees.

Games

11

# Cretaceous period

The Cretaceous lasted around 80 million years, and by the time it was over the Earth had become a very different place from the early days of the Triassic.

## STICK

the stickers of Earth in the circles, then add dinosaur stickers to the continents.

Pentaceratops

Titanosaurus

Giganotosaurus

Add the Triassic world sticker here.

### Triassic Earth

Toward the end of the Triassic, the supercontinent Pangaea began to break up into several smaller landmasses.

Add the Jurassic world sticker here.

### Jurassic Earth

The newly-formed continents drifted apart during the Jurassic, creating large shallow seas.

### Cretaceous Earth

During the Cretaceous, the supercontinent Pangaea split further apart and Earth's continents began to look more like they do today.

### Modern Earth

Today the Earth is divided into seven continents. They're still moving – it just happens so slowly that it's hard to tell.

13

Which type am I?

# Different types of dinosaur

**Dinosaurs**

**Saurischians**
One type of dinosaurs, saurischians, were called "lizard-hipped".

An example of a saurischian's hip.

**Theropods**
(THERRO-pods)
A group of meat-eaters that **walked on two legs**, theropods had strong jaws and curved teeth to help them chew meat.

**Sauropodomorphs**
(SORE-oh-POD-oh-morfs)
This group of plant-eaters had very **long necks and tails**, and were the biggest animals to ever walk the Earth.

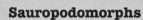

**Thyreophorans**
(THIGH-ree-OFF-oh-rans)
These plant-eaters were famous for having impressive **armoured plates** and spikes.

**Ornithischians**
The other type, ornithischians, were called "bird-hipped" dinosaurs.

**Ornithopods**
(OR-nith-oh-pods)
A very common group of dinosaurs, ornithopods reached for food with their beaks and cropping teeth.

**Marginocephalians**
(MAR-jee-no-sa-FAY-lee-ans)
Famous for their **frills and horns**, this group of plant-eaters were common during the Cretaceous period.

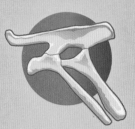

An example of an ornithischian's hip.

Dinosaurs came in all shapes and sizes, but there were only two main types (based on their hip bones). These dinosaurs could then be split up into five smaller groups.

FOLLOW the lines and write down which type of dinosaur each one is.

**Ouranosaurus**

I am an _ _ _ _ _ _ _ _ _ _ _ _ _ _ _ _ _ _ _ _

**Huayangosaurus**

I am a _ _ _ _ _ _ _ _ _ _ _ _ _ _ _ _ _ _ _ _

**Argentinosaurus**

I am a _ _ _ _ _ _ _ _ _ _ _ _ _ _ _ _ _ _ _ _

**Triceratops**

I am a _ _ _ _ _ _ _ _ _ _ _ _ _ _ _ _ _ _ _ _

**Timimus**

I am a _ _ _ _ _ _ _ _ _ _ _ _ _ _ _ _ _ _ _ _

Wow, these are long names!

Games

15

# Sticker gallery

### Allosaurus
This predator from the Jurassic had very sharp teeth.

### Pentaceratops
The sharp horns on its head helped it to defend itself.

### Edmontonia
Its body was covered in sharp, armoured spikes.

### Sauropods
These giants often lived by rivers and coasts.

## STICK
the correct stickers for each frame in the right place.

### Corythosaurus
The crest on its head could have been used to "talk" to its herd.

**DRAW** your favourite dinosaur and write its name in the box.

# Age of the dinosaurs

The dinosaurs as we think of them became extinct 65 million years ago, but to this day they still fascinate us. How many of these facts about them did you know?

Don't forget to put your stickers in first.

Page _____

Page _____

Page _____

**FIND** these pictures on pages 20–33 and write the page numbers in the boxes.

Page _____

Page _____

Page _____

**STICK** the sticker that matches each creature and read the facts about each one.

# 1 Quetzalcoatlus

With a massive wingspan 12m (39ft) across, Quetzalcoatlus was the largest creature to ever fly.

**12m**

# 2 Spinosaurus

It was actually Spinosaurus, not Tyrannosaurus rex, who was the largest meat-eater to ever walk the Earth.

# 4 Diplodocus

The gigantic sauropod Diplodocus could grow to be up to 35m (115ft), and its long tail contained around 80 bones.

Solid bone dome!

# 3 Archaeopteryx

About the same size as a modern raven, Archaeopteryx was the first known bird.

Around **80** bones

*Quizzes*

# 5 Suchomimus

This dinosaur had a long snout and claws, which were useful for catching fish.

# 6 Pachycephalosaurus

This plant-eater had a solid dome on its head that it would use like a battering ram to fight off enemies and rivals.

# Flying high with
# pterosaurs

While dinosaurs ruled the land, pterosaurs owned the sky. These flying reptiles usually had hollow bones and small bodies, but could have wingspans of up to 11m (36ft).

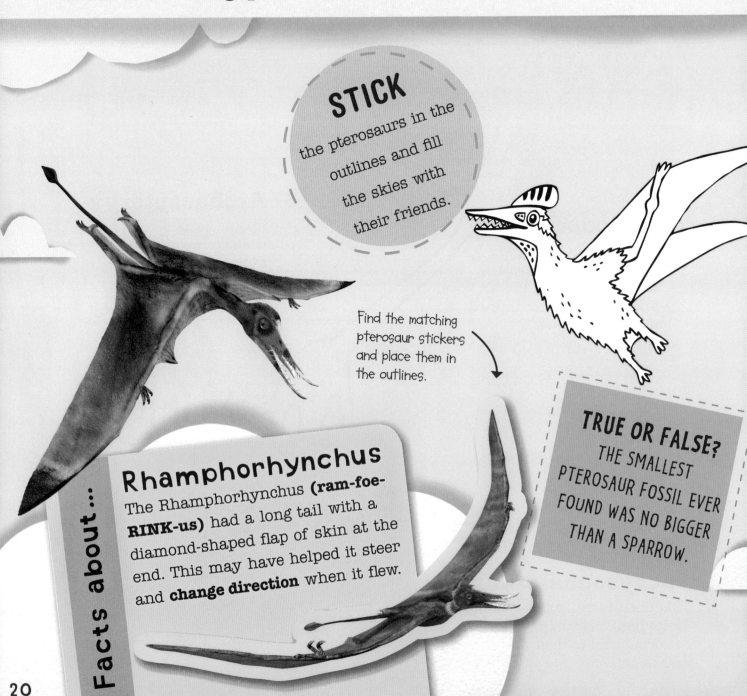

**STICK** the pterosaurs in the outlines and fill the skies with their friends.

Find the matching pterosaur stickers and place them in the outlines.

### Facts about...
## Rhamphorhynchus
The Rhamphorhynchus **(ram-foe-RINK-us)** had a long tail with a diamond-shaped flap of skin at the end. This may have helped it steer and **change direction** when it flew.

**TRUE OR FALSE?**
THE SMALLEST PTEROSAUR FOSSIL EVER FOUND WAS NO BIGGER THAN A SPARROW.

## Facts about...

### Dimorphodon

Its unusually large head was about a third of its body length, and contained two types of teeth – perfect for trapping prey.

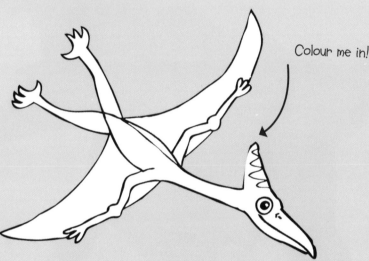

Colour me in!

## Facts about...

### Pteranodon

This pterosaur was given its name (pteranodon means "**wing without tooth**") after fossil collectors discovered it had **no teeth** at all.

## Facts about...

### Pterodactylus

One of the best known pterosaurs, it had a short tail and long neck, and its wings were covered in a leathery material which helped it to **fly quickly**.

# The mixed-up scrap book

Oops! Someone has mixed up the labels in their dinosaur scrapbook. Can you use the clues on the tags to figure out which is which?

### Suchomimus
- Had a narrow hump along its back.
- Its head looked a bit like a crocodile's.
- Walked on its hind legs.
- Had a long, slender skull.

### Giganotosaurus
- Had short forearms with sharp claws.
- A relative of T. rex.
- Walked on strong hind legs.
- Had razor-sharp teeth.

### Dimorphodon
- Had a large head and beak.
- Its tail was fairly thin.
- Is actually a pterosaur, not a dinosaur.
- Its wings were made of skin.

### Mamenchisaurus
- Walked on four legs.
- Was a herbivore.
- Had one of the longest necks of any animal in history.
- Had a strong thick hide.

**1**

### Pentaceratops
- Was a herbivore.
- Walked on four legs.
- Had a large beak.
- Used its horns for defence.
- Had a large, armoured skull.

**2**

**3**

# Are you a dino BRAIN BOX or a dino DUNCE?

## MATCH

the descriptions to each dinosaur and write their names in the boxes.

**4**

**5**

23

**TRUE OR FALSE?**
MARINE REPTILES
ARE DINOSAURS
THAT SWIM.

2

1

3

**STICK**
the marine reptiles
in the right spot, then
match them to the
descriptions.

# Under the sea

Dinosaurs were land-based creatures, but during the time they walked the land, another group of creatures called marine reptiles lurked beneath the ocean waves.

## Facts about... Pliosaurus

This giant beast (seen below) grew to up to 12m (40ft) and was one of the deadliest marine reptiles of all time. Until 2012 it was referred to as **"Predator X"**.

**4**

### Ichthyosaurus
• Had a small, slim snout.
• Its body was shaped a bit like a dolphin's.
• Had fairly large eyes for its size.

### Metriorhynchus
• It looked a little like a prehistoric crocodile.
• Had a long, powerful tail with a large fin at the back.

### Elasmosaurus
• Its neck was as long as the whole of its body.
• Its head was very small compared to its body.
• Had four large flippers.

### Lariosaurus
• It had paddles instead of front legs, with claws at the back.
• Its tail was thin, with no fin at the back.

Write the number for each answer here.

25

# Dino sticker puzzles

## STICK
the stickers into the grids to match the dinosaur pictures.

Dinosaurs come in all shapes and sizes. How well do you think you can tell them apart? Find out with these sticker puzzles.

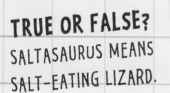

**TRUE OR FALSE?**
SALTASAURUS MEANS SALT-EATING LIZARD.

## Facts about...

## Saltasaurus

This herbivore from the Late Cretaceous was one of the last of the dinosaurs. It grazed on plants and had a **thick hide** that helped to protect it from predators.

## Saltasaurus

Spinosaurus

## Bigger than T. rex!!!

### How big?

It may not be as famous as T. rex, but growing to up to 18m (60ft) long, Spinosaurus was the **largest predator** to ever walk on land.

## Spinosaurus

Facts about...

This massive predator from the Late Cretaceous was best known for the large **sail-like spine** on its back. It feasted on fish, birds, turtles, and other dinosaurs.

27

# A-**maze**-ing escape!

Life wasn't always easy for a dinosaur. Some of them, such as Tenontosaurus, couldn't easily defend themselves from attackers, and hungry predators could be lurking around every corner!

START

Colour me in

## DRAW

a safe route through the maze, then tick the box by each predator you spot.

Colour me in

I only eat plants, but these dinosaurs are scary!

**Tenontosaurus**
ten-NON-toe-SORE-us
# END

Well done! But now I'm hungry...

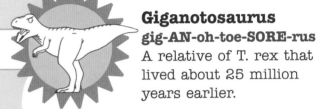

How do you say the names of these dinosaurs?

# Hungry predators

### Tyrannosaurus rex
**TIE-ran-oh-SORE-us**
The king of dinosaurs, and maybe the most fearsome predator of all.

### Giganotosaurus
**gig-AN-oh-toe-SORE-rus**
A relative of T. rex that lived about 25 million years earlier.

### Utahraptor
**YOU-tah-RAP-tor**
Most famous for its deadly claws, it was a fierce hunter.

### Carnotaurus
**CAR-no-TAWR-us**
A fairly large predator with thick horns above its eyes.

### Deinonychus
**dye-NON-ee-cuss**
A small, but deadly pack hunter from the Cretaceous period.

### Spinosaurus
**SPINE-oh-SORE-us**
The largest predator to ever walk the Earth.

Games

# How many dinosaurs?

Do you have a keen eye? There are three species of dinosaur on these pages. How many of each type can you spot?

**WRITE** down the total number of T. rex you can spot.

T. rex

## Facts about...

### T. rex

Also known as Tyrannosaurus rex, it stood at 4m (13ft) tall and 12m (40ft) long, making it one of the most **ferocious beasts** to ever live.

Barosaurus

## Facts about... Barosaurus

Standing at a massive 26m (40ft) long, Barosaurus was a plant-eating giant from the Jurassic period that used its **long tail** like a whip to fight back against attackers.

**WRITE** down the total number of Barosaurus you can spot.

Stegosaurus

**WRITE** down the total number of stegosaurus you can spot.

## Facts about... Stegosaurus

The **bony plates** along its back look scary, but Stegosaurus only ate plants. That doesn't mean it couldn't put up a fight – its massive **spiky tail** was deadly to any attackers.

Games

# Sticker gallery

**Theropods**
These meat-eaters were the deadly hunters of the dinosaur age.

**Pterodactylus**
One of the best-known pterosaurs. It had a short neck and long tail that helped it fly.

**Archaeopteryx**
About the size of a pigeon, Archaeopteryx was the first bird.

**STICK**
the correct stickers for each frame in the right place.

**Barapasaurus**
Unlike most sauropods, Barapasaurus had sharp saw-like teeth.

**Nothosaurus**
A fast agile swimmer, this reptile hunted in the seas but could also walk on land.

**COLOUR** the scene and write a description in the box.

# Dinosaur life

Even though the world was a very different place when dinosaurs existed, in a lot of ways dinosaurs had more in common with modern animals than you might think.

Don't forget to put your stickers in first.

Page ____

Page ____

Page ____

**FIND** these pictures on pages 36–49 and write the page numbers in the boxes.

Page ____

Page ____

Page ____

the stickers and write if you think each dinosaur is a carnivore or herbivore.

## Herbivore or carnivore?

Just like modern animals, different dinosaurs ate different foods. Dinosaurs that only ate plants were called **herbivores**, and ones that also ate fish, insects, and other dinosaurs were called **carnivores**.

**1 Carcharodontosaurus**

This massive dinosaur had teeth similar to some sharks.

All carnivores walked on two legs, but so did some herbivores.

**2 Carnotaurus**

This dinosaur could run quickly. But did it chase other dinosaurs, or run away from them?

**3 Euoplocephalus**

Covered from head to toe in armour, this powerful dinosaur also had a heavy tail club to defend itself.

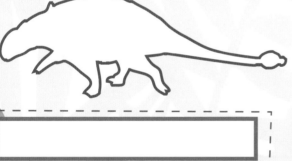

**4 Saltasaurus**

This dinosaur's long neck helped it to reach for leaves in tall trees.

**5 Hypsilophodon**

It was about the size of a modern deer, and loved to eat plants.

Carnivores had sharp teeth to help them eat.

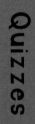

Quizzes

35

# Who gets dinner?

Only some dinosaurs could defend themselves against attackers – and if they couldn't run away they would end up being another dinosaur's dinner!

FIND ☑

which path leads to the dinosaur in the middle and tick the box.

## Facts about...

### Utahraptor

One of the deadliest dinosaurs of the Early Cretaceous, Utahraptor had a huge **hooked claw** on its hind feet that it would use to attack its prey.

## Facts about...

### Iguanodon

The plant-eating Iguanodon was about the same size as an elephant, and used its sharp **thumb-like spike** to defend itself from other dinosaurs.

END

# Copy the SCENE

COPY the picture below on to the next page. Try starting in the corners.

Are you a budding artist? By copying each square in this grid you'll be able to draw a great dinosaur scene in no time.

Which of these dinosaurs can you spot in the image?

Edmontonia

Triceratops

Diplodocus

T. rex

Pterodactylus

Stegosaurus

1 - - - - - - - - - - - - - - - - - - - -

2 - - - - - - - - - - - - - - - - - - - -

3 - - - - - - - - - - - - - - - - - - - -

4 - - - - - - - - - - - - - - - - - - - -

# Home sweet home

Dinosaurs lived in several different places (habitats). There were six main types, and where they lived depended on the climate or how much food there was.

## Mountains

There probably wasn't much food, but dinosaur fossils have been found near mountains.

## Forests

The trees in forests were a rich source of food for many plant-eaters.

## Swampland

Swamps were perfect for both fish-eating and plant-eating dinosaurs.

I liked to be in wet areas with trees and fish.

There weren't that many plants where I lived.

I lived in a very hot, dry, and dusty place.

**1**

**2**

**3**

Spinosaurus lived in the...

Swampland

Plateosaurus lived in the...

Gallimimus lived in the...

## Desert plains

The Earth was hotter than it is today, with vast deserts all over. Some dinosaurs adapted to live there.

**MATCH** the dinosaurs to the habitats based on the clues at the bottom.

## Riverbanks

All living things need water to survive, so a lot of dinosaurs lived by rivers and coasts.

Add more dinosaurs to the scene using stickers.

## Scrubland

Not too many plants grew here, but scrubland was home to many early dinosaurs.

I sometimes lived high up, by lots of rocks.

The place I lived had plenty of water.

There were lots of tasty trees where I lived.

**4**

**5**

**6**

Edmontonia lived in the...

Herrerasaurus lived in the...

Stegosaurus lived in the...

# Hunter and hunted

For carnivores (meat-eaters), dinner was often another dinosaur! Sometimes smaller dinosaurs made a meal of one much bigger than themselves.

Start

## Deinonychus

This ferocious hunter from the Early Cretaceous is named "terrible claw" because of the deadly claws on its feet.

**CONNECT** the dots to reveal the rest of the picture, then colour it in.

Games

## Hunting

When taking on a bigger dinosaur, a group of smaller predators may have **ganged up** to attack it together. Many modern animals such as hyenas and wolves do this too.

Facts about...

43

# Save the eggs

A Maiasaura has been separated from her babies. Find something to use as counters and help guide her back to her nest.

## Start
Roll a dice and move the correct number of steps along the board.

## 10
### Egg fact
Some species of dinosaur would sit on their nests in a similar way chickens do today.

## 9
A Brachiosaurus offers you a shortcut, **go forward** to step 22.

## 8

## 11

## 12
You're being chased! Climb a vine to escape and **go back** to step 1.

## 13

## 14
You get slowed down by a passing herd. **Miss a** turn.

## 15

Finish

## 24
An Ankylosaur is blocking you path. **Roll a six to end the game**

**1**

**2**

**3**
Slide down the Barosaurus' neck and **go forward** to step 19.

**4**
Hitch a ride on a Pterodactylus. On your next turn, **roll again.**

**7**
You hear a deadly T. rex nearby. **Go back** to step 2 and hide.

**6**

**5**

**16**
You take a break and feel rested. **Roll again**.

**17**
**Egg fact**
Scientists weren't always sure that dinosaurs laid eggs until a fossilized nest was found in China in 1920.

**18**

**19**

**23**

**22**

**21**
You're almost crushed by a Barosaurus! **Miss a turn.**

**20**

# What **colour** were they?

As fossils (remains of prehistoric life) are made of stone, even experts can't be fully sure what colour dinosaurs were. But by studying other animals we can get a few ideas.

**COLOUR**

in the dinosaurs. Read the facts to help you decide how to make them look.

## Facts about...

### Blending in

Some animals blend into the environment while hunting prey. A tiger's stripes keep it **hidden in tall grass**. Some dinosaurs may have been able to blend in too.

## Facts about...

### Standing out

Peacocks and some other animals are colourful so they can **attract a mate** or threaten enemies. It's possible some dinosaurs also had ways of standing out.

## Facts about...

### Being plain

Animals such as elephants **don't have any predators**, so don't need to blend in or stand out. It's likely many dinosaurs were plain as well.

47

# Sticker gallery

**STICK** the correct stickers for each frame in the right place.

**Herds**
Hadrosaurs and other dinosaurs often travelled in large herds.

**Hunting**
Certain dinosaurs may have attacked in groups while hunting.

**Eggs**
Some dinosaurs would sit on their eggs the same way birds do.

**Fishing**
Baryonyx and other dinosaurs would stalk rivers looking for fish.

→ **COPY** the picture of the Baryonyx fishing and give your drawing a name.

# Studying **dinosaurs**

Experts called palaeontologists dedicate their lives to studying fossils (the remains of prehistoric creatures) so that we can all learn more about these amazing creatures.

Don't forget to put your stickers in first.

Page _____

Page _____

**FIND**
these pictures on pages 52–64 and write the page numbers in the boxes.

Page _____

Page _____

Page _____

Page _____

Page _____

50

# TEST

*yourself to see how much you know about fossils. Don't forget to read the facts, too!*

## Plants

It's not just dinosaurs that become fossils. Plants and other animals can too.

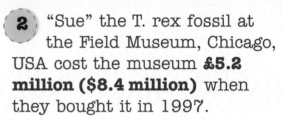

## Bones

In rare cases, entire skeletons are found preserved in rock.

## Ammonites

Creatures from the ocean could also become fossils.

## Footprints

Fossilized footprints give experts clues about how big dinosaurs could be.

## TRUE OR FALSE ?

**1** The experts whose job it is to study fossils are called **dinologists?**

TRUE ◯  FALSE ◯

**2** "Sue" the T. rex fossil at the Field Museum, Chicago, USA cost the museum **£5.2 million ($8.4 million)** when they bought it in 1997.

TRUE ◯  FALSE ◯

**3** Fossils are **very common**, and you can buy them in most shops.

TRUE ◯  FALSE ◯

**4** In ancient China, dinosaur fossils were believed to be the remains of **dragons**.

TRUE ◯  FALSE ◯

**5** The oldest fossils ever found are **1 billion years old**.

TRUE ◯  FALSE ◯

**6** **Teeth** are the most commonly found fossils.

TRUE ◯  FALSE ◯

Quizzes

51

# The great extinction

**COLOUR** in the picture on the right side of the page.

Dinosaurs ruled the Earth for millions of years. But 65 million years ago, a giant meteorite struck the Earth causing them to become extinct.

## How it happened

The meteorite struck the Earth with such force that it caused earthquakes, tsunamis, volcanic eruptions, and threw a cloud of dust into the sky, blocking out the Sun.

Scientists think the meteorite was about 10km (6 miles) wide!

*"Extinct" means "no longer existing".*

## Are they all gone?

While dinosaurs as we think of them are all gone, modern birds are their direct descendents – making birds the only **surviving dinosaurs**!

Small mammals like this Nemegtbaatar survived.

## Facts about...

### Survivors

No land animals bigger than a dog survived the mass extinction, but other animals such as fish, lizards, insects, and a few small mammals did.

# How fossils are made...

It takes a very long time for fossils to form, and some of the earliest discovered are almost 3.5 billion years old!

## COLOUR

the rest of the comic to finish off the story of fossilization.

## Facts about...

### Fossilization

Living things can only become fossils if they are **buried quickly** after death. Otherwise they simply decay and disappear. This is why fossils are so rare.

### TRUE OR FALSE?

SEA CREATURES CAN'T TURN INTO FOSSILS.

70 million years ago...

**1** A dinosaur has died and its body quickly sinks into thick mud, burying it and protecting it from the elements.

2 million years ago...

**4** The Earth's plates have shifted even more and a mountain range has formed above the fossil.

**Five years later...**

**2** Its flesh has slowly rotted away leaving just the bones – which have split apart and are buried under the ground.

**50 million years ago...**

**3** The Earth's plates have shifted and a sea has spread over the area. Pressure has made the mud and sand harden.

**Present day...**

What's that over there in the sand?

It looks like a bone, but it's so big!

**5** Over a long period of time, the mountains and other layers on top of the fossil have been worn away by extreme weather. Then one day a bone is spotted and palaeontologists can dig up the pieces of the fossil.

# Dinosaurs and their fossils

Fossils are remains of things that lived long ago that have turned to stone and been preserved in the Earth. Scientists study them to learn about prehistoric life.

Who am I?

Who am I?

Write the fossil letters heres.

**A** T. rex

**B** Deinonychus

## Stone clues

Without fossils we would know very little about dinosaurs and prehistoric life. By **studying fossils**, scientists can find clues about a dinosaur's size, shape, diet, and more.

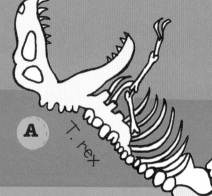

Fossil experts are called palaeontologists.

# STICK
the dinosaurs into the outlines and match them to their fossils.

Who am I?

Who am I?

Match the stickers to these shapes.

Who am I?

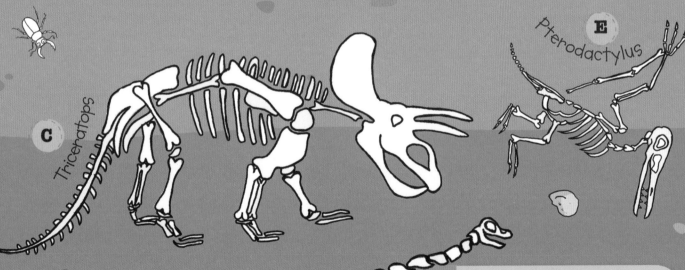

Pterodactylus

**E**

Triceratops

**C**

**D**

Brachiosaurus

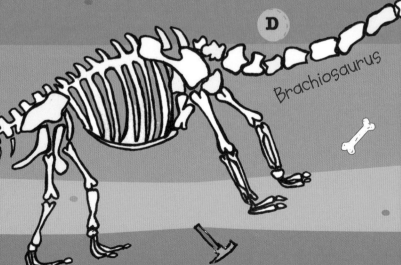

Facts about...

# Excavation
It can be a very long and difficult job to get fossils out of the ground because they can be stuck between layers of hard rock that has to be broken up bit by bit.

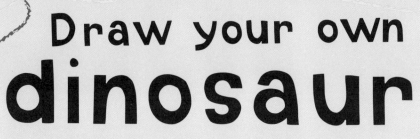

# Draw your own
# dinosaur

Drawing a dinosaur might seem hard, but it's not if you break it into steps. Get started by drawing this little Compsognathus.

## Step 1

Start by lightly copying this frame in pencil to work out how big your dinosaur will be. Add circles for the head, body, and limbs as shown.

## Step 2

Draw the outline of your dinosaur, using the circles as a guide. Don't worry about adding detail yet – just focus on the basic shape.

## Step 3

Use an eraser to get rid of the guides. Add details such as claws, eyes, and teeth. Finally, colour it in!

I'm about the same size as a Compsognathus!

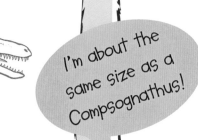

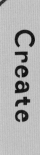

**DRAW** a compsognathus in the space below. Don't forget to practise!

**Facts about...**

## Compsognathus

One of the smallest predators ever was **Compsognathus (COMP-sog-NAITH-us)**, which was only about the size of a big chicken! Amazingly, despite its size, it could run at speeds of up to a blazing 40kph (25mph)!

59

# Dino dig notes

With so many species of dinosaur, pterosaur, and marine reptile, experts take notes to help them keep track. Add the pictures to help finish off the research.

## Piatnitzkysaurus
(PEA-at-NITS-key-SORE-us)

- **LENGTH:** Up to 4m (13ft)
- **FOUND IN:** Forests
- **FOOD:** Meat
- **LIVED:** Middle Jurassic

## STICK
the stickers in the right places. Use the shapes as a guide.

## Albertosaurus
(al-BERT-oh-SORE-us)

- **LENGTH:** Up to 9m (30ft)
- **FOUND IN:** Forests
- **FOOD:** Meat
- **LIVED:** Late Cretaceous

## Mosasaurus
(MOSE-ah-saw-rus)

- **LENGTH:** Up to 15m (50ft)
- **FOUND IN:** Oceans
- **FOOD:** Fish, squid, shellfish
- **LIVED:** Late Cretaceous

## Cryolophosaurus
(CRY-oh-loaf-oh-SAWR-us)

- **LENGTH:** Up to 8m (26ft)
- **FOUND IN:** Plains
- **FOOD:** Meat
- **LIVED:** Early Jurassic

## Ouranosaurus
(ooh-RAN-uh-SAWR-us)

- **LENGTH:** Up to 7m (23ft)
- **FOUND IN:** Desert plains
- **FOOD:** Plants
- **LIVED:** Early Cretaceous

## Efraasia
(E-FRAHS-ee-A)

- **LENGTH:** Up to 7m (23ft)
- **FOUND IN:** Forests
- **FOOD:** Plants
- **LIVED:** Late Triassic

## Heterodontosaurus
(HET-er-oh-DON-toe-SORE-us)

- **LENGTH:** Up to 1m (3ft)
- **FOUND IN:** Scrubland
- **FOOD:** Plants
- **LIVED:** Early Jurassic

## Mamenchisaurus
(ma-MEN-chee-SORE-uss)

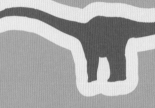

- **LENGTH:** Up to 26m (85ft)
- **FOUND IN:** Forest plains
- **FOOD:** Plants
- **LIVED:** Late Jurassic

## Elasmosaurus
(el-LAZZ-moe-SORE-us)

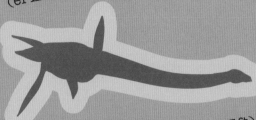

- **LENGTH:** Up to 14m (45ft)
- **FOUND IN:** Oceans
- **FOOD:** Fish, squid, shellfish
- **LIVED:** Late Cretaceous

## Ichthyosaurus
(ICK-thee-oh-SORE-uss)

- **LENGTH:** Up to 2m (6ft)
- **FOUND IN:** Oceans
- **FOOD:** Fish
- **LIVED:** Early Jurassic

**STICK**

the missing pieces of the skeleton back on to fix the fossil.

# Fix the
# fossil

Museums all over the world have amazing fossil collections you can go and visit. Seeing dinosaur skeletons up close gives you a much better idea of how big they were.

## Parasaurolophus

Pronounced PA-ra-SORE-oh-LOAF-US, is famous for its **long, curved skull**, which it might have used like a trumpet to warn its herd of danger.

Parasaurolophus could walk on its hind legs or on all fours.

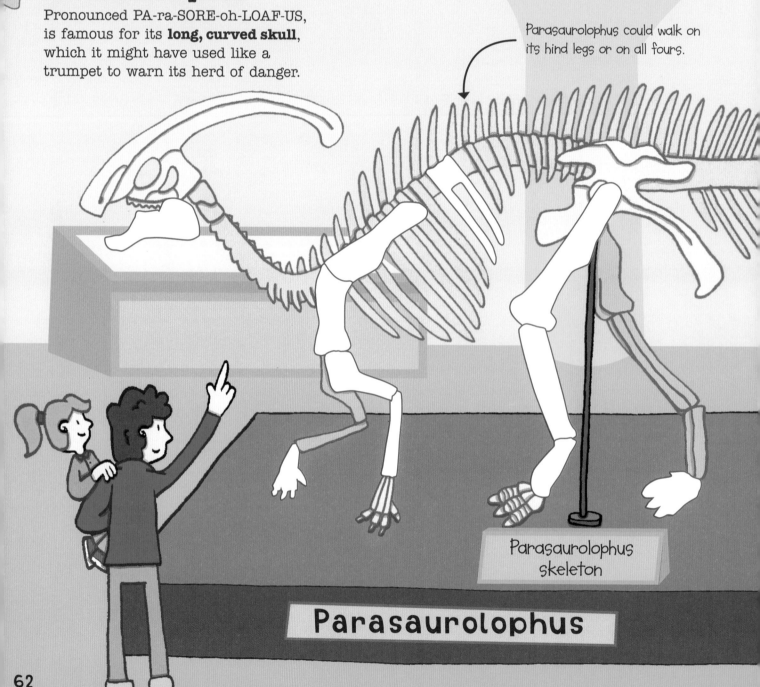

Parasaurolophus skeleton

Parasaurolophus

# Which hadrosaur head is that?

**1** **Corythosaurus** had a small snout with a rounded crest at the top of its head.

**2** **Lambeosaurus** had a narrow mouth and a crest that resembled an axe blade.

**3** **Brachylophosaurus** had a deep snout and a rectangle-shaped skull that was flat on top.

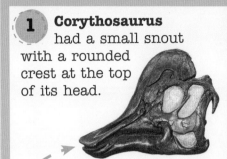

Find the **STICKERS** that match the skulls.

Challenges

All hadrosaurids had strong, stiff tails.

Colour in the Parasaurolophus model.

Parasaurolophus model

## Facts about...

# Hadrosaurids

Parasaurolophus belonged to a group of dinosaurs called hadrosaurids. This group of plant-eating dinosaurs from the Late Cretaceous were famous for their strange heads and **duck-like bills**.

# Sticker gallery

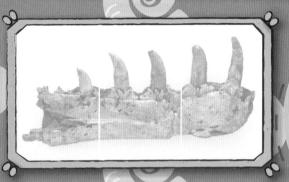

## STICK
the correct stickers for each frame in the right place.

### Teeth
The most commonly found fossils are usually teeth.

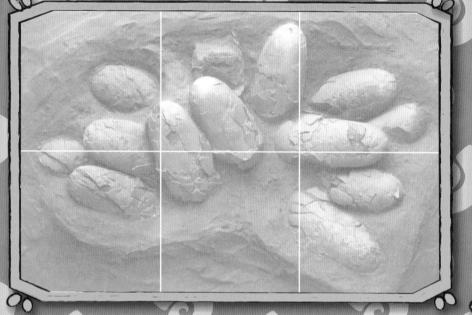

### Feathers
Fossils like this show scientists that some dinosaurs had feathers.

### Eggs
We know dinosaurs laid eggs because scientists have found their fossils.

### Coprolites
The name for fossilized poo, these give us clues about a creature's diet.

### Skulls
The size of a dinosaur's skull can help us figure out a dinosaur's size.

Use the colours as clues to where to place these dinosaurs on **page 8.**

Fill the scene on **pages 8–9** with these dinosaurs (plus extras to use however you want!)

These stickers belong on **pages 12–13**.

These ones are extras, use them for decoration if you want.

Decorate the pages of the book with these!

Piece together these sticker puzzles on **page 16**.

These are extras for fun or decoration.

Stick these slippery sea monsters on **pages 24–25**.

Use these extra ones anywhere you like.

Solve this puzzling dinosaur jigsaw on **page 27**...

...And this one on **page 26**.

Stickers

75

Find the place for these on **page 19**. The small ones are extras.

These stickers belong on **page 32** as well.

Stick these fearsome pterosaurs on **pages 20–21**.

These ones belong on **page 32**.

Stick these carnivores and herbivores on **page 35**.

Here are some footprints and other extras to use however you like.

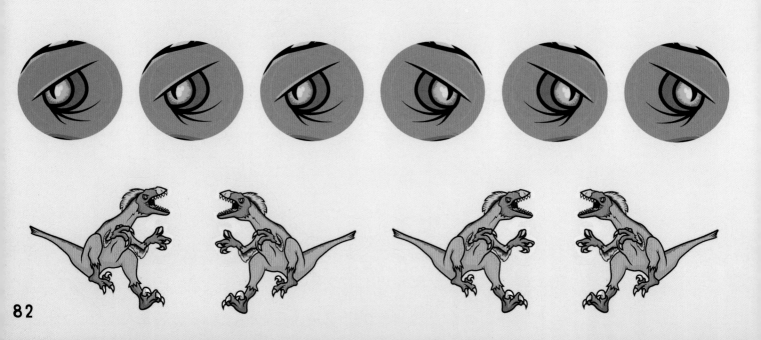

Add these dinosaurs to their habitats on **pages 40–41**. There are some spares too.

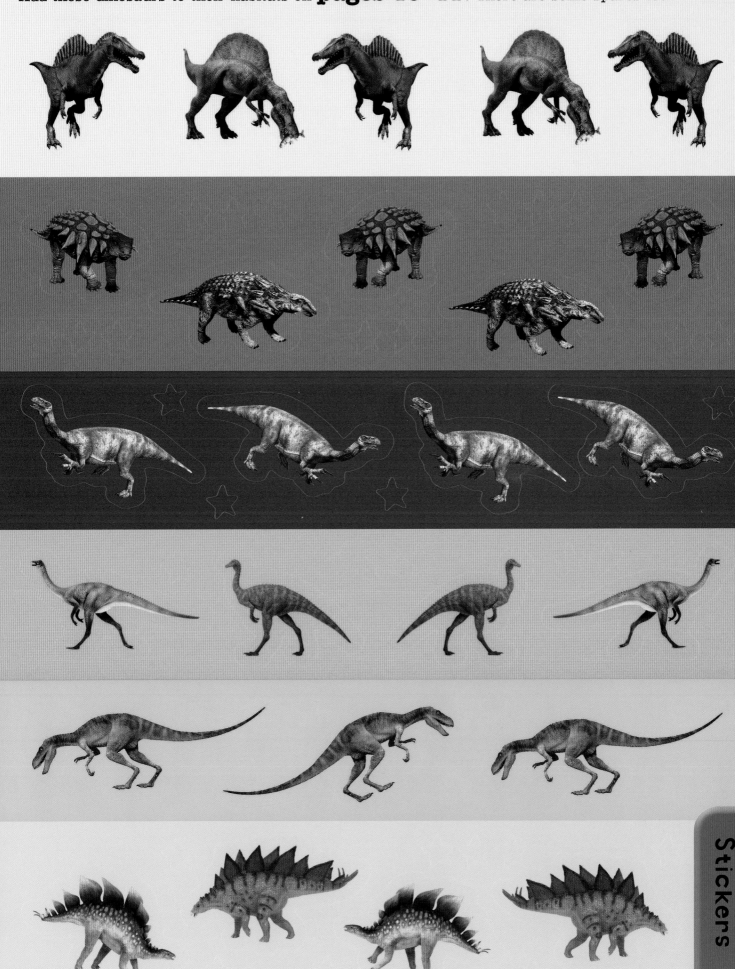

Stick these ones wherever you like!

These stickers are for the puzzles on **page 48**.

These footprints and skulls are spares to use wherever you like.

Place these stickers on **pages 56–57**.

Use these dino footprints anywhere you like.

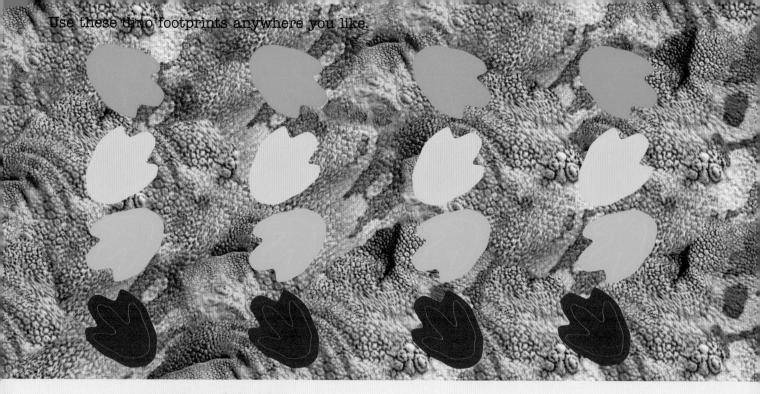

Use these on **pages 62–63**. The bottom three are extras.

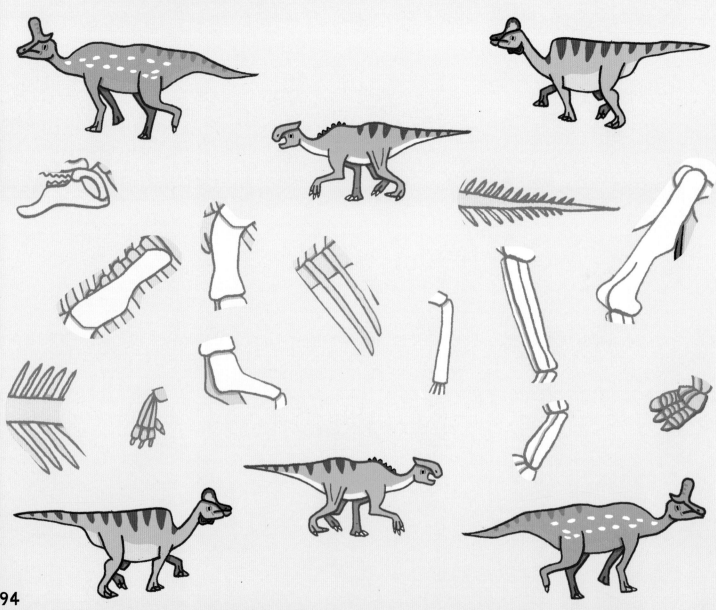

94

What will you do with these spare fossils?